Mommy Goes to Heaven

Written By: Alicia H. Watson

Illustrated By: Sameer Kassar

W0007312

Dedication

In *loving* memory of my *mother*, **Esther Bell-Watson!**

I miss you everyday!

"Mommy, please don't go to heaven.
If you leave, I'll be here all alone.
Who will take care of me?
If you go away, you will forever be gone."

"Mommy, I wish I could heal you and take all your pain away.

I wish I could understand why you must leave me today."

"Mommy, it's so hard to say goodbye to you.
I feel so very sad inside, no matter what I do."

"Mommy, you're leaving too early and your life can't be done.

What am I to do without you when my life has barely begun?"

"Mommy, I know that I am sad, and I may not understand.

But, I choose to hold on to what you taught me about God and His unchanging hand."

"Mommy, I remember when you told me that God will always make a way.

And, although this pain feels too great, I choose to trust God today."

"Mommy, it's time for you to go to the other side of your destiny.

Jump into God's loving arms freely without hesitancy."

"Mommy, I know that you must move on and I will be strong.

I've heard that heaven is a wonderful place.

And, deep down inside, I know it's where you truly belong."

"Mommy, do not worry because I will be okay.
Heaven is gaining an angel in you today."

"Mommy, I will pray as you taught me every night before I go to sleep.

I know God is watching and I know He hears me."

"Mommy, I know God loves you more than I ever could.

So, I know He will take care of you, just like a Father should."

"Mommy, I love you. I know it's time to let you go.
But, I will always carry you in my heart, as I
continue to grow."

"Mommy, I will be strong and remember all the lessons that you taught me.

You are the best mommy in the whole wide world, and I will forever be grateful because of your great love towards me."

"God, please take care of mommy for me.
I know she's in your hands.
I know how much you love her.
Mommy's going to heaven, and God, I understand."

The End

About the author:

Alicia Watson is an author, blogger, literacy educator, and speaker. She travels the world motivating people to believe and to pursue their dreams and purpose in life. Visit her website today at www.elevatedinspiration.com.

Made in the USA
Las Vegas, NV
06 March 2024